Who Moved My [illegible]

An Amazing [illegible]
In Your [illegible]

"This is the first bu[illegible] [illegible]ead that I expect to re-read [illegible] [illegible] a regular basis in discussions with personnel, friends and customers. I bought 25 copies and shared this book with my father-in-law, brother-in-law and son. They all agreed it was a great story and an excellent way to motivate people to work through change."

Bruce Crager, Senior VP
Oceaneering International Inc

"Every once in a while a book comes along that opens a door to the future. *Who Moved My Cheese?* had that effect on me. Spencer Johnson opened my eyes to the changes streaking by me which I couldn't as yet identify. Must reading for the New Millennium."

David A. Heenan, Board Member
Peter F. Drucker Graduate Management Center
Author, The New Corporate Frontier

"This wonderful story has great application for all types and ages of people. I can picture myself reading it to my children and grand children in our family room with a warm fire glowing, and their understanding the lessons taught in these pages."

Lt. Col. Wayne Washer, Lead, Mission Systems
Aeronautical Science Center, Wright Patterson AFB

"*Who Moved My Cheese?* creates a language to discuss risk and change on a lighter note ... the message is clear ... and the characters in the book can be found in all industries. The book will be used throughout our training."

Sally Grumbles, Director of Customer Operations
BellSouth Mobility Inc., N. Fl

Who
Moved
My
Cheese?

Books by Spencer Johnson, M.D.

THE ONE MINUTE MANAGER (with Kenneth Blanchard, Ph.D.)
THE PRECIOUS PRESENT: The Gift That Makes You Happy Forever
THE ONE MINUTE $ALES PERSON (with Larry Wilson)
THE ONE MINUTE MOTHER
THE ONE MINUTE FATHER
THE ONE MINUTE TEACHER (with Constance Johnson, M.Ed.)
ONE MINUTE FOR MYSELF
"YES" OR "NO": The Guide to Better Decisions

THE VALUETALES SERIES FOR CHILDREN
THE VALUE OF BELIEVING IN YOURSELF:The Story of Louis Pasteur
THE VALUE OF PATIENCE:The Story Of The Wright Brothers
THE VALUE OF KINDNESS:The Story Of Elizabeth Fry
THE VALUE OF HUMOR:The Story Of Will Rogers
THE VALUE OF COURAGE:The Story Of Jackie Robinson
THE VALUE OF CURIOSITY:The Story Of Christopher Columbus
THE VALUE OF IMAGINATION:The Story Of Charles Dickens
THE VALUE OF SAVING:The Story Of Ben Franklin
THE VALUE OF SHARING:The Story Of The Mayo Brothers
THE VALUE OF HONESTY:The Story Of Confucius
THE VALUE OF UNDERSTANDING:The Story Of Margaret Mead
THE VALUE OF FANTASY:The Story Of Hans Christian Anderson
THE VALUE OF DEDICATION:The Story Of Albert Schweitzer

WHO MOVED MY CHEESE?

An Amazing Way To Deal With Change In Your Work And In Your Life

Spencer Johnson

PRIVATELY PUBLISHED EDITION

Dedicated to my friend, Dr. Kenneth Blanchard,
whose enthusiasm encouraged me to write this book,
and whose help brought it to so many people.

WHO MOVED MY CHEESE?

For pre-publication information:
Tel: (808) 637-9030
Fax: (808) 637-7505

Who Moved My Cheese?

CONTENTS

The Story Behind The Story
by Kenneth Blanchard, Ph.D.

I am thrilled to be telling you 'the story behind the story' of *Who Moved My Cheese?,* because it means the book has now been written, and is available for us to read over and over again, and to share with others.

This is something I've wanted to see happen ever since I first heard Spencer Johnson tell his great 'Cheese' story, years ago, before we wrote our book *The One Minute Manager* together. I remember thinking then how good the story was and I've used what I learned from it ever since.

It is a story about change that takes place in a Maze where four amusing characters look for 'Cheese', a metaphor for what we want to have in life, whether it is a job, a relationship, money, a big house, freedom, health, recognition, spiritual peace, or even an activity like jogging or golf.

Each of us has our own idea of what Cheese is, and we pursue it because we believe it makes us happy. If we get it, we often become attached to it. And if we lose it, or it's taken away, it can be traumatic.

The 'Maze' in the story represents where you spend time looking for what you want. It can be the organization you work in, the society you live in, or the relationships you have in your life.

I tell the Cheese story you are about to read in my talks around the world, and hear later from people who tell me what a difference it has made to them.

Believe it or not, this little story has been credited with saving careers, marriages and lives!

One of many examples comes from Charlie Jones, a well-respected broadcaster for NBC-TV, who revealed that hearing the story of 'Who Moved My Cheese?' saved his career. His job is unique but the principles can be used by anyone.

Here's what happened: Charlie had worked hard and had done a great job of broadcasting Track and Field events at an earlier Olympic Games, so he was surprised and upset when his boss told him he'd been removed from these showcase events for the next Olympics and assigned to Swimming and Diving.

Not knowing these sports as well, he was frustrated, felt unappreciated and he was angry. It wasn't fair! His anger began to affect everything he did.

Then, he heard the story of 'Who Moved My Cheese?'

After hearing the story, he said he laughed at himself and changed his attitude. He saw his boss had just 'moved his Cheese.' So he adapted, learned the two new sports, and found that doing something new made him feel young.

It wasn't long before his boss recognized his new attitude and energy, and he soon got better assignments. He went on to enjoy more success than ever and was later inducted into Pro Football's Hall of Fame—Broadcasters' Alley.

That's just one of the many real-life stories we've heard about the impact this story has had on people from their work life to their love life.

We all work and live in changing times and so our 'Cheese' is always being moved.

In business, companies that were once household names are now gone. These companies wanted loyalty; today's companies need your help. They need flexible people who are not possessive about "the way things are done around here."

Adaptability to change is a key success trait for both people and organizations to survive, let alone succeed, in today's global economy. Those who can adapt are the ones who are rewarded.

Most successful managers know this and strive to create environments that help people change and *enjoy* it. As the rate of change increases, we all need to adapt to change more than ever.

Unexpected changes, at work or in life, can be stressful, as you know, unless you have a way of looking at change that helps you understand it, which is what the 'Cheese' story does. This brief parable takes little time to read, but the insights can last you for a lifetime.

As you turn the pages, you will find three sections in this book. In the first, *A Gathering*, former classmates talk at a class reunion about trying to deal with the changes happening in their lives. The second section is *The Story of Who Moved My Cheese?*, the core of the book. And in the third part, *A Discussion*, several people discuss what they got out of *The Story* and how they plan to use it in their lives.

Some readers of this book's early manuscript preferred to stop at the end of *The Story*, without reading further, and interpret its meaning for themselves. Others enjoyed reading *A Discussion* at the end because it stimulated their thinking about how they might apply what they'd learned.

In any case, I hope each time you reread *Who Moved My Cheese?* you will find something new and useful in it, as I do, and that it will help you deal with change and bring you success, whatever you decide success is for you.

I hope you enjoy what you discover and I wish you well.

Ken Blanchard
San Diego, 1998

Who
Moved
My
Cheese?

The best laid schemes
o' mice and men
often go astray.

Robert Burns
1759-1796

A Gathering
Chicago

One sunny Sunday in Chicago, several former classmates gathered for lunch, having attended their high school reunion the night before. They wanted to hear more about what was happening in each others lives. After a good deal of kidding, and a good meal, they settled into a conversation.

Angela, who had been one of the most popular people in the class said, “Life sure turned out differently than I thought it would when we were in school. A lot has changed.”

“It certainly has,” Nathan echoed. They knew he had gone into his family’s business, which had operated pretty much the same, and had been a part of the local community for as long as they could remember. So, they were surprised when he seemed concerned. He asked, “But, have you noticed how we don’t want to change when things change?”

Carlos said, “I guess we resist changing, because we’re afraid of change.”

“Carlos, you were Captain of the football team,” Jessie said. “I never thought I’d hear you say anything about being afraid!”

They all laughed as they realized that although they had gone off in different directions—from working at home to managing companies, they were experiencing similar feelings.

Everyone was trying to cope with the unexpected changes that were happening to them in recent years. And most admitted that they did not know a good way to handle them.

Then Michael said, "I used to be afraid of change. When a big change came along in our business, we didn't know what to do. So we didn't do anything differently and we almost lost it.

"That is," he continued, "until I heard a funny little story that changed everything."

"How so?" Nathan asked.

"Well, the story altered the way I looked at change, and after that, things quickly improved for me—at work and in my life.

"Then, I passed the story on to some people in our company and they passed it on to others, and soon our business did much better, because we all adapted to change better. And like me, many people said it helped them in their personal lives."

"What's the story?" Angela asked.

"It's called, 'Who Moved My Cheese?'"

The group laughed. "I think I like it already," Carlos said. "Would you tell *us* the story?"

"Sure," Michael replied. "I'd be happy to—it doesn't take long." And so he began:

The Story

ONCE, long ago in a land far away when times were different, there were four little characters who ran through a maze looking for cheese to nourish them and make them happy.

Two were mice, named "Sniff" and "Scurry" and two were littlepeople—beings who were as small as mice but who looked and acted a lot like people today. Their names were "Hem" and "Haw."

Due to their small size, it was easy not to notice what the four of them were doing. But if you looked closely enough, you could discover the most amazing things!

Everyday the mice and the littlepeople spent time in the maze looking for their own special cheese.

The mice, Sniff and Scurry, possessing only simple rodent brains, but good instincts, searched for the hard nibbling cheese they liked, as mice often do.

The two littlepeople, Hem and Haw, used their brains, filled with many beliefs, to search for a very different kind of Cheese—with a capital C—which they believed would make them feel happy and successful.

As different as the mice and littlepeople were, they shared something in common: every morning, they each put on their jogging suits and running shoes, left their little homes, and raced out into the maze looking for their favorite cheese.

The maze was a labyrinth of corridors and chambers, some containing delicious cheese. But there were also dark corners and blind alleys leading nowhere. It was an easy place for anyone to get lost.

However, for those who found their way, the maze held secrets that let them enjoy a better life.

The mice, Sniff and Scurry, used the simple, but inefficient, trial-and-error method of finding cheese. They ran down one corridor and if it proved empty, they turned and ran down another.

Sniff would smell out the general direction of the cheese, using his great nose, and Scurry would race ahead. They got lost, as you might expect, went off in the wrong direction and often bumped into walls.

However, the two littlepeople, Hem and Haw, used a different method that relied on their ability to think and learn from their past experiences, although, they would sometimes get confused by their beliefs and emotions.

Eventually in their own way, they all discovered what they were looking for—they each found their own kind of cheese one day at the end of one of the corridors in Cheese Station C.

Every morning after that, the mice and the littlepeople dressed in their running gear and headed over to Cheese Station C.

It wasn't long before a routine set in.

Sniff and Scurry continued to wake early every day and race through the maze, always following the same route.

When they arrived at their destination, the mice took off their running shoes, tied them together and hung them around their necks—so they could get to them quickly whenever they needed them again. Then they enjoyed the cheese.

A different routine set in for the littlepeople. Hem and Haw awoke each day a little later, dressed a little slower, and walked to Cheese Station C. After all, they knew where the Cheese was now and how to get there.

They had no idea where the Cheese came from. They just assumed it would be there.

As soon as Hem and Haw arrived at Cheese Station C each morning, they settled in and made themselves at home. They hung up their jogging suits and put away their running shoes for good because they felt they wouldn't need them again, now that they had found the Cheese.

"This is great," Hem said. "There's enough Cheese here to last us forever." The littlepeople felt happy and successful, and thought they were now secure.

It wasn't long before Hem and Haw regarded the Cheese they found at Cheese Station C as *their* cheese. It was such a large store of Cheese that they eventually moved their homes to be closer to it, and built a social life around it.

To make themselves feel more at home, Hem and Haw decorated the walls with sayings and even drew pictures of Cheese around them which made them smile. One read:

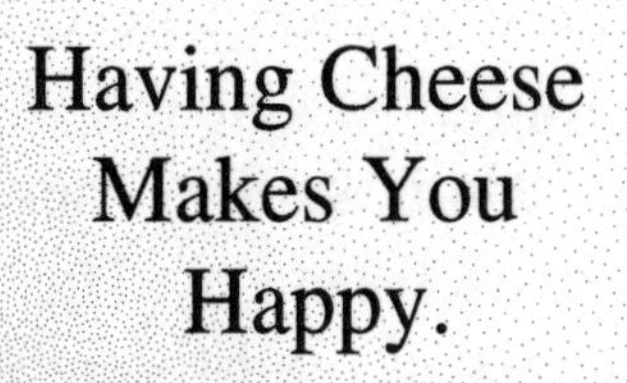
Having Cheese
Makes You
Happy.

Sometimes Hem and Haw would take their friends by to see their pile of Cheese at Cheese Station C, and point to it with pride, saying, "Pretty nice Cheese, huh?" Sometimes they shared it with their friends and sometimes they didn't.

"We deserve this Cheese," Hem said. "We certainly had to work long and hard enough to find it." He picked up a nice fresh piece and ate it.

Afterwards, Hem fell asleep, as he often did.

Every night the littlepeople would waddle home, full of Cheese, and every morning they would confidently return for more.

This went on for quite some time.

After a while Hem and Haw's confidence grew into arrogance. Soon they became so comfortable they didn't even notice what was happening.

As time went on, Sniff and Scurry continued their routine. They arrived early each morning and sniffed and scratched and scurried around Cheese Station C, inspecting the area to see if there had been any changes from the day before. Then they would sit down to nibble on the cheese.

One morning they arrived at Cheese Station C and discovered there was no cheese.

They weren't surprised. Since Sniff and Scurry had noticed the supply of cheese had been getting smaller every day, they were prepared for the inevitable and knew instinctively what to do.

They looked at each other, removed the running shoes they had tied together and hung conveniently around their necks, put them on their feet and laced them up.

The mice did not overanalyze things. And they were not burdened with many complex beliefs.

To the mice, the problem and the answer were both simple. The situation at Cheese Station C had changed. So, Sniff and Scurry decided to change.

They both looked out into the maze. Then Sniff lifted his nose, sniffed, and nodded to Scurry, who took off running through the maze, while Sniff followed as fast as he could.

They were quickly off in search of new cheese.

Later that same day, Hem and Haw arrived at Cheese Station C. They had not been paying attention to the small changes that had been taking place each day, so they took it for granted their Cheese would be there.

They were unprepared for what they found.

"What! No Cheese?" Hem yelled. He continued yelling, "No Cheese? No Cheese?" as though if he shouted loud enough someone would put it back.

"Who moved my Cheese?" he hollered.

Finally, he put his hands on his hips, his face turned red, and he screamed at the top of his voice, "It's not fair!"

Haw just shook his head in disbelief. He, too, had counted on finding Cheese at Cheese Station C. He stood there for a long time, frozen with shock. He was just not ready for this.

Hem was yelling something, but Haw didn't want to hear it. He didn't want to deal with what was facing him, so he just tuned everything out.

The littlepeoples' behavior was not very attractive or productive but it was understandable.

Finding Cheese wasn't easy, and it meant a great deal more to the littlepeople than just having enough of it to eat everyday.

Finding Cheese was the littlepeoples way of getting what they thought they needed to be happy. They had their own ideas of what Cheese meant to them, depending on their taste.

For some, finding Cheese was having material things. For others it was enjoying good health, or developing a spiritual sense of well being.

For Haw, Cheese just meant feeling safe, having a loving family someday and living in a cozy cottage on Cheddar Lane.

To Hem, Cheese was becoming A Big Cheese in charge of others and owning a big house atop Camembert Hill.

Because Cheese was important to them, the two littlepeople spent a long time trying to decide what to do. All they could think of was to keep looking around Cheeseless Station C to see if the Cheese was really gone.

While Sniff and Scurry had quickly moved on, Hem and Haw continued to hem and haw.

They ranted and raved at the injustice of it all. Haw started to get depressed. What would happen if the Cheese wasn't there tomorrow? He had made future plans based on this Cheese.

The littlepeople couldn't believe it. How could this have happened? No one had warned them. It wasn't right. It was not the way things were supposed to be.

Hem and Haw went home that night hungry and discouraged. But before they left, Haw wrote on the wall:

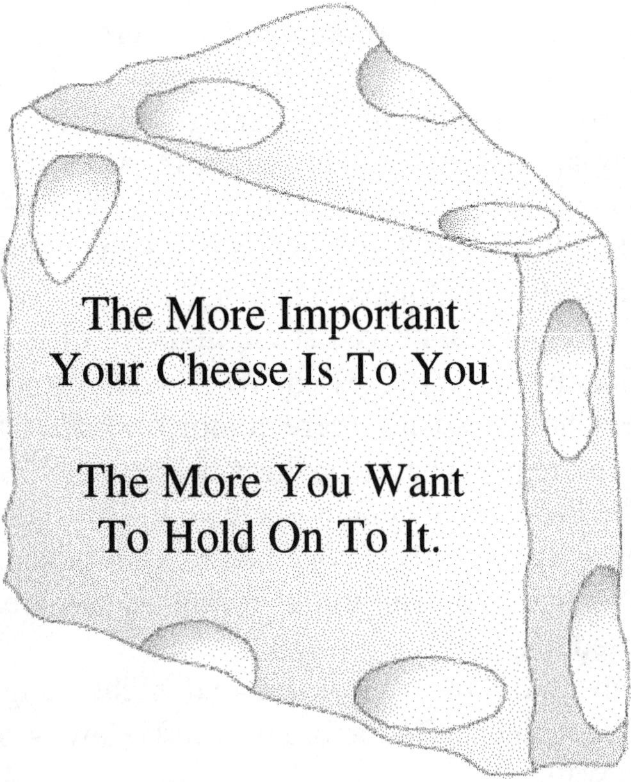

The More Important
Your Cheese Is To You

The More You Want
To Hold On To It.

The next day Hem and Haw left their homes, and returned to Cheese Station C again, where they still expected, somehow, to find *their* Cheese.

The situation hadn't changed, the Cheese was no longer there. The littlepeople didn't know what to do. Hem and Haw just stood there, immobilized like two statues.

Haw shut his eyes as tight as he could and put his hands over his ears. He just wanted to block everything out. He didn't want to know the Cheese supply had gradually been getting smaller. He believed it had been moved all of a sudden.

Hem analyzed the situation over and over and eventually his complicated brain with it's huge belief system took hold. "Why did they do this to me?" he demanded. "What's really going on here?"

Finally, Haw opened his eyes, looked around and said, "By the way, where are Sniff and Scurry? Do you think they know something we don't?"

Hem scoffed, "What would they know?"

"They're just simple mice. They just respond to what happens. We're littlepeople. We're special. We should be able to figure this out. And, besides, we deserve better.

"This should not happen to us, or if it does, we should at least get some benefits."

"Why should we get benefits?" Haw asked.

"Because we're entitled," Hem claimed.

"Entitled to what?" Haw wanted to know.

"We're entitled to our Cheese."

"Why?" Haw asked.

"Because, we didn't cause this problem," Hem said. "Somebody else did this and we should get something out of it."

Haw suggested, "Maybe we should stop analyzing the situation so much and just get going and find some New Cheese."

"Oh no," Hem argued. "I'm going to get to the bottom of this."

While Hem and Haw were still trying to decide what to do, Sniff and Scurry were already well on their way. They went farther into the maze, up and down corridors, looking for cheese in every Cheese Station they could find.

They didn't think of anything else but finding new cheese.

They didn't find any for sometime until they finally went into an area of the maze where they had never been before: Cheese Station N.

They squealed with delight. They found what they had been looking for: a great supply of new cheese.

They could hardly believe their eyes. It was the biggest store of cheese the mice had ever seen.

In the meantime, Hem and Haw were still back in Cheese Station C evaluating their situation. They were now suffering from the effects of having no Cheese. They were becoming frustrated and angry and were blaming each other for the situation they were in.

Now and then Haw thought about his mice buddies, Sniff and Scurry, and wondered if they had found any cheese yet. He believed they might be having a hard time, as running through the maze usually involved some unpleasantness. But he also knew that it was likely to last for only a while.

Sometimes, Haw would imagine Sniff and Scurry finding new cheese and enjoying it. He thought about how good it would be for him to be out on an adventure in the maze, and to find fresh New Cheese. He could almost taste it.

The more clearly Haw saw the image of himself finding and enjoying the New Cheese, the more he saw himself leaving Cheese Station C.

"Let's go!" he exclaimed, all of a sudden.

"No," Hem quickly responded. "I like it here. It's comfortable. It's what I know. Besides it's dangerous out there."

"No it isn't," Haw argued. "We've run through many parts of the maze before, and we can do it again."

"I'm getting too old for that," Hem said. "And I'm afraid I'm not interested in getting lost and making a fool of myself. Are you?"

With that, Haw's fear of failing returned and his hope of finding New Cheese faded.

So everyday, the littlepeople continued to do what they had done before. They went to Cheese Station C, found no Cheese, and returned home, carrying their worries and frustrations with them.

They tried to deny what was happening, but found it harder to get to sleep, had less energy the next day, and were becoming irritable.

Their homes were not the nurturing places they once were.

But they still returned to Cheese Station C and waited there every day.

"We'll just sit here and see what happens," Hem would say. "Sooner or later they have to put the Cheese back."

Haw wanted to believe that. So the littlepeople simply went home and came back to Cheese Station C. They arrived earlier and stayed longer, but it was always the same. The Cheese never reappeared.

By now, they were growing weak from hunger and stress and Haw was getting tired of just waiting for their situation to improve. He knew the longer they stayed in their Cheeseless situation the worse off they would be.

Haw knew they were losing their edge.

Finally, one day Haw began laughing at himself. "Haw, haw, look at me. I keep doing the same things over and over again and wonder why things don't get better. If this wasn't so ridiculous, it would be even funnier."

Haw did not like the idea of having to run through the maze again, because he knew he would get lost and have no idea where he would find any Cheese. But he had to laugh at his folly when he saw what his fear was doing to him.

He asked Hem, "Where did we put our jogging suits and running shoes?" It took a long time to find them because they had put everything away when they found their Cheese at Cheese Station C, thinking they wouldn't be needing them anymore.

As Hem saw his friend getting into his running gear, he said, "You're not really going out into the maze again, are you? Why don't you just wait here with me until they put the Cheese back?"

"Because, you just don't get it," Haw said. "I didn't want to see it either, but now I realize they're never going to put the Old Cheese back. That was yesterday's Cheese. It's time to find New Cheese."

Hem argued, "But what if there is no Cheese out there? Or even if there is, what if you don't find it?"

"I don't know," Haw said. He had asked himself those same questions too many times and started to feel the fears again that kept him where he was.

Then he thought about finding New Cheese and all the good things that came with it and gathered his courage.

"Sometimes," Haw said, "things change and they are never the same again. This looks like one of those times, Hem. That's life! Life moves on. And so should we."

Haw looked at his emaciated companion and tried to talk sense to him, but Hem's fear had turned into anger and he wouldn't listen.

Haw didn't mean to be rude to his friend, but he had to laugh at how silly they had both looked.

As Haw prepared to leave, he started to feel more alive, knowing that he was finally able to laugh at himself, let go and move on.

He announced, "It's maze time!"

Hem didn't laugh and he didn't respond.

Haw picked up a small, sharp rock and wrote a serious thought on the wall for Hem to think about. As was his custom, Haw even drew a picture of cheese around it, hoping it would help Hem to smile, lighten up, and go after the New Cheese. But Hem didn't want to see it.

It read:

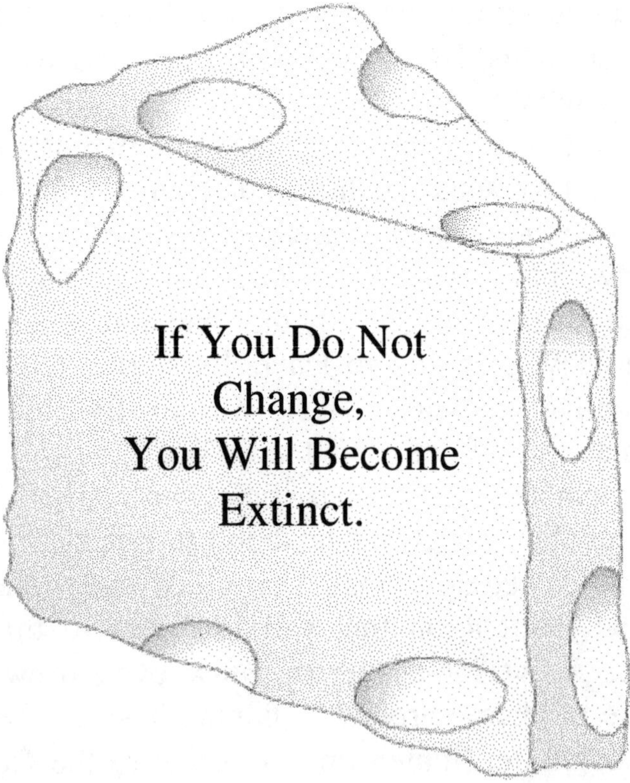

If You Do Not
Change,
You Will Become
Extinct.

Then, Haw stuck his head out and peered anxiously into the maze. He thought about how he'd gotten himself into this cheeseless situation.

He had believed that there may not be any Cheese in the maze, or he may not find it. Such fearful beliefs were immobilizing and killing him.

Haw smiled. He knew Hem was wondering, "Who moved my Cheese?" but Haw was wondering, "Why didn't I get up and move with the Cheese, sooner?"

As he started out into the maze, Haw looked back to where he had come from and felt its comfort. He could feel himself being drawn back into familiar territory—even though he hadn't found Cheese there for some time.

Haw became more anxious and wondered if he really wanted to go out into the maze. He wrote a saying on the wall ahead of him and stared at it for some time:

What Would You Do
If You Weren't Afraid?

He thought about it.

He looked to his right, to the part of the maze where he had never been, and felt the fear.

Then, he took a deep breath, turned right into the maze, and jogged slowly, into the unknown.

As he tried to find his way, Haw worried, at first, that he may have waited too long in Cheese Station C. He hadn't had any Cheese for so long that he was now weak. It took him longer and it was more painful than usual, to get through the maze. He decided that if he ever got the chance again, he would adapt to change sooner. It would make things easier.

Then, Haw smiled a weak smile as he thought, "Better late than never."

During the next several days, Haw found a little Cheese here and there, but nothing that lasted very long. He had hoped to find enough Cheese to take some back to Hem and encourage him to come out into the maze.

But Haw didn't feel confident enough yet. He had to admit, he found it confusing in the maze. Things seemed to have changed since the last time he was out here.

Just when he thought he was getting ahead, he would get lost in the corridors. It seemed his progress was two steps forward and one step backwards. It was a challenge, but he had to admit that being back in the maze, hunting for Cheese, wasn't nearly as bad as he feared it might be.

As time went on he began to wonder if it was realistic for him to expect to find New Cheese. He wondered if he had bitten off more than he could chew. Then he laughed, realizing that he had nothing to chew on at the moment.

Whenever he started to get discouraged he reminded himself that what he was doing, as uncomfortable as it was at the moment, was in reality, much better than staying in the Cheeseless situation. He was taking control, rather than simply letting things happen to him.

Then he reminded himself, if Sniff and Scurry could move on, so could he!

LATER, as Haw looked back on things, he realized that the Cheese at Cheese Station C had not just disappeared overnight, as he had once thought. The amount of Cheese that had been there towards the end had been getting smaller, and what was left had grown old. It didn't taste as good.

Mold may even have begun to grow on the Old Cheese, although he hadn't noticed it. He had to admit however, that if he had wanted to, he probably could have seen what was coming. But he didn't.

Haw now realized that the change probably would not have taken him by surprise if he had been watching what was happening all along and if he had anticipated change. Maybe that's what Sniff and Scurry had been doing.

He stopped for a rest and wrote on the wall of the maze :

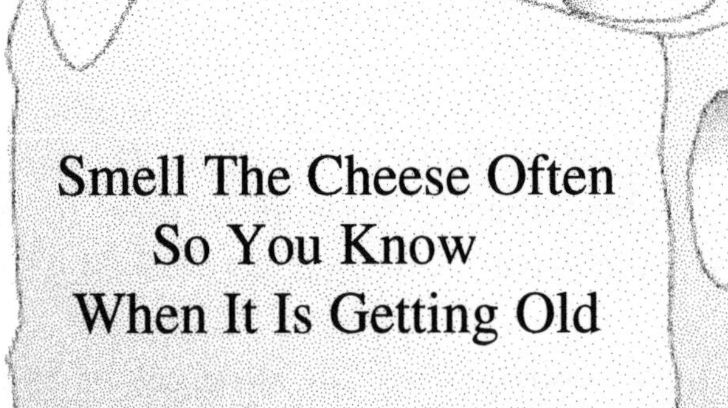
Smell The Cheese Often
So You Know
When It Is Getting Old

SOMETIME later, after not finding Cheese for what seemed like a long time, Haw finally came across a huge Cheese Station which looked promising. When he went inside however, he was most disappointed to discover that the Cheese station was empty.

"This empty feeling has happened to me too often," he thought. He felt like giving up.

Haw was losing his physical strength. He knew he was lost and was afraid he would not survive. He thought about turning around and heading back to Cheese Station C. At least, if he made it back, and Hem was still there, Haw wouldn't be alone. Then he asked himself the same question, again "What would I do if I weren't afraid?"

He was afraid more often than he liked to admit, even to himself. He wasn't always sure what he was afraid of, but, in his weakened condition, he knew now he was simply fearful of going on alone. Haw didn't know it, but he was running behind because he was weighed down by fearful beliefs.

Haw wondered if Hem had moved on, or if he was still paralyzed by his fears. Then, Haw remembered the times when he had felt his best in the maze. It was when he was moving along.

He wrote on the wall, knowing it was as much a reminder to himself, as it was a marking for his buddy Hem, hopefully, to follow:

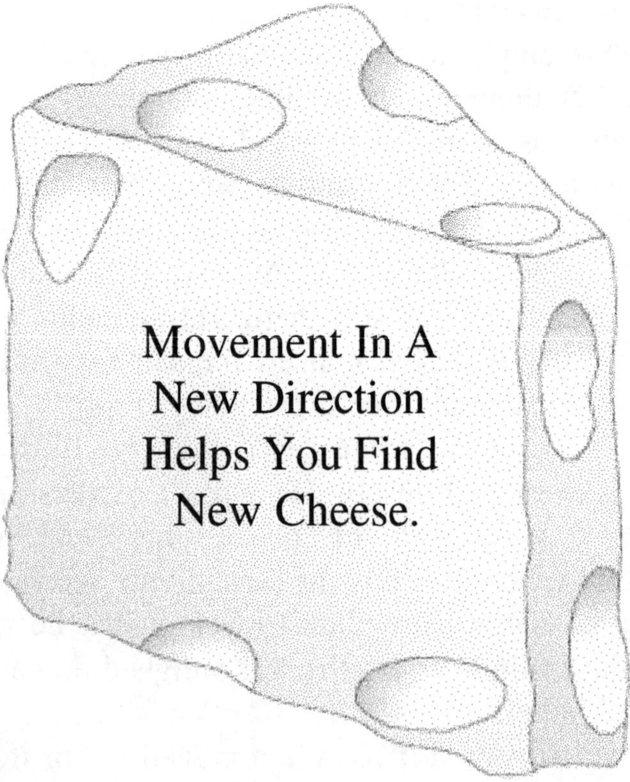

Movement In A
New Direction
Helps You Find
New Cheese.

Haw looked down the dark passageway and was aware of his fear. What lay ahead? Was it empty? Or worse, were there dangers lurking? He began to imagine all kinds of frightening things that could happen to him. He was scaring himself to death.

Then he laughed at himself. He realized his fears were making things worse. So he did what he would do if he wasn't afraid. He moved in a new direction.

As he started running down the dark corridor he began to smile. Haw didn't realize it yet, but he was discovering what nourished his soul. He was letting go and trusting what lay ahead for him, even though he did not know exactly what it was.

To his surprise, Haw started to enjoy himself more and more. "Why do I feel so good?" he wondered. "I don't have any Cheese and I don't know where I am going."

Before long, he knew why he felt good.

He stopped to write again on the wall:

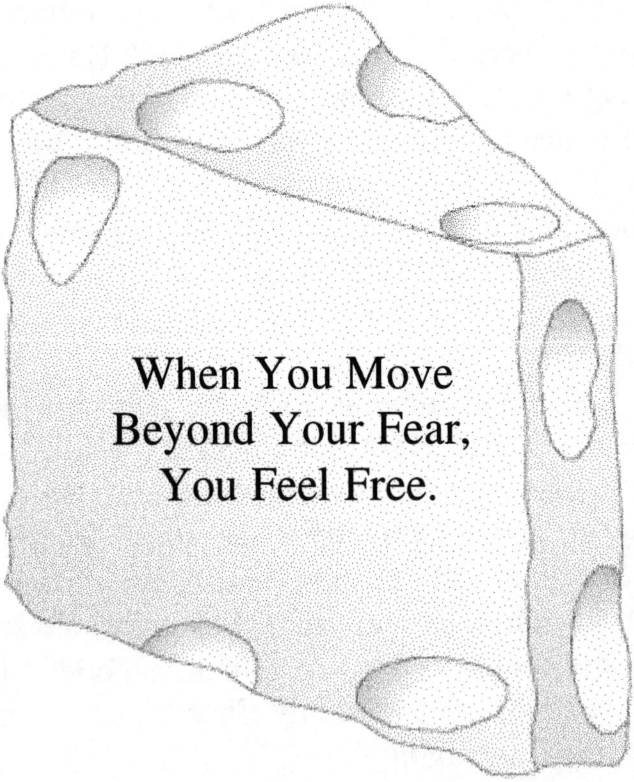

When You Move
Beyond Your Fear,
You Feel Free.

Haw felt the cool breeze that was blowing in this part of the maze and it was refreshing. He took in some deep breaths and felt invigorated by the movement. Once he had gotten past his fear, it turned out to be more enjoyable than he once believed it could be.

He hadn't felt this way for a long time. He had almost forgotten how much fun it was.

To make things even better, Haw started to paint a picture in his mind. He saw himself in great realistic detail, sitting in the middle of a pile of all his favorite cheeses—from Velveeta to Brie! He saw himself eating the many cheeses he liked, and he enjoyed what he saw. Then he imagined how much he would enjoy all their great tastes.

The more clearly he saw the image of New Cheese, the more real it became, and the more he could sense that he was going to find it.

He wrote:

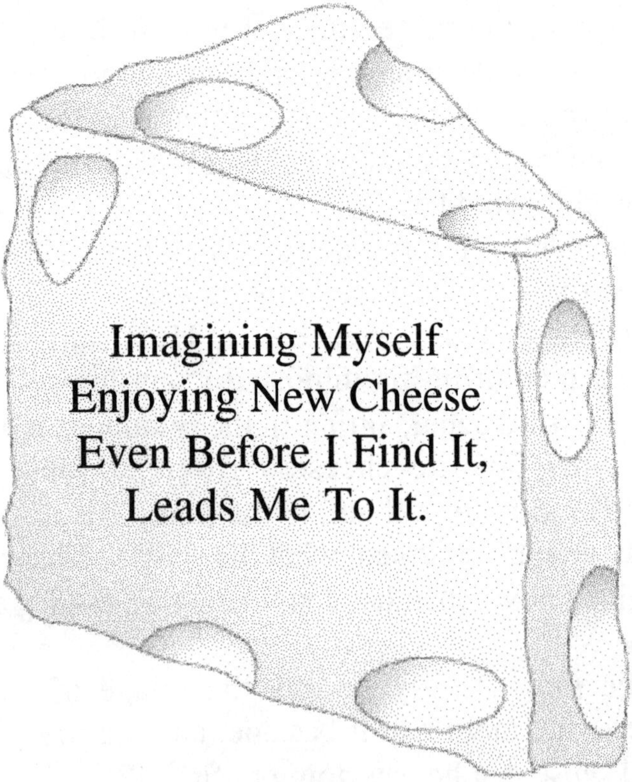

Imagining Myself
Enjoying New Cheese
Even Before I Find It,
Leads Me To It.

"Why didn't I do this before?" Haw asked himself.

Then he raced through the maze with greater strength and agility. Before long he spotted a Cheese Station and became excited as he noticed little pieces of New Cheese near the entrance.

They were types of Cheeses he had never seen before, but they looked great. He tried them and found that they were delicious. He ate most of the New Cheese bits that were available and put a few in his pocket to have later and, perhaps share with Hem. He began to regain his strength.

He entered the Cheese Station with great excitement. But, to his dismay, he found it was empty. Someone had already been there and had left only the few bits of New Cheese.

He realized that if he had moved sooner, he would very likely have found a good deal of New Cheese here.

Haw decided to go back and see if Hem was ready to join him.

As he retraced his steps, he stopped and wrote on the wall:

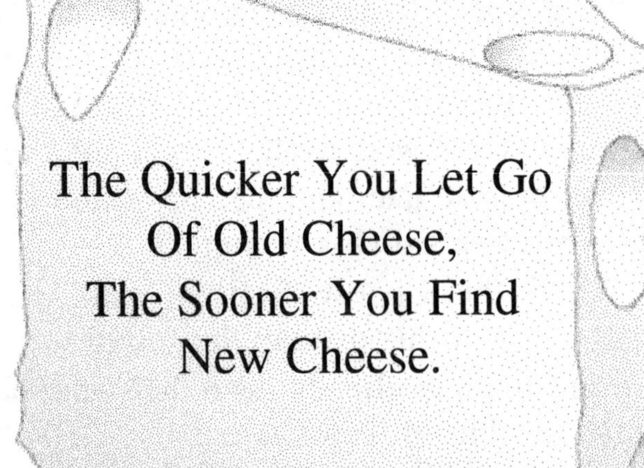
The Quicker You Let Go
Of Old Cheese,
The Sooner You Find
New Cheese.

After a while Haw found his way back to Cheese Station C and found Hem. He offered him bits of New Cheese, but was turned down.

Hem appreciated his friend's gesture, but he said he didn't think he would like New Cheese. It was just not what he was used to. He was still going to wait until the Old Cheese was put back.

Haw just shook his head in disappointment and reluctantly went back out on his own. As he returned to the farthest point he had reached in the maze, he missed his friend, but realized he liked what he was discovering. Even before he found what he hoped would be a great supply of New Cheese, if ever, he knew that what made him happy wasn't just having Cheese.

He was happy with what he was doing now.

He realized again, as he had once before, that what you are afraid of is never as bad as what you imagine. The fear *you let* build up in your mind is worse than the situation that actually exists.

Knowing this, Haw didn't feel as weak as he did when he stayed in Cheese Station C with no Cheese. Just realizing that he was not letting his fear stop him, knowing that he had taken a new direction, nourished him and gave him strength.

Now he knew that it was just a question of time before he found what he needed. In fact, he felt he had already found it.

He smiled, as he realized:

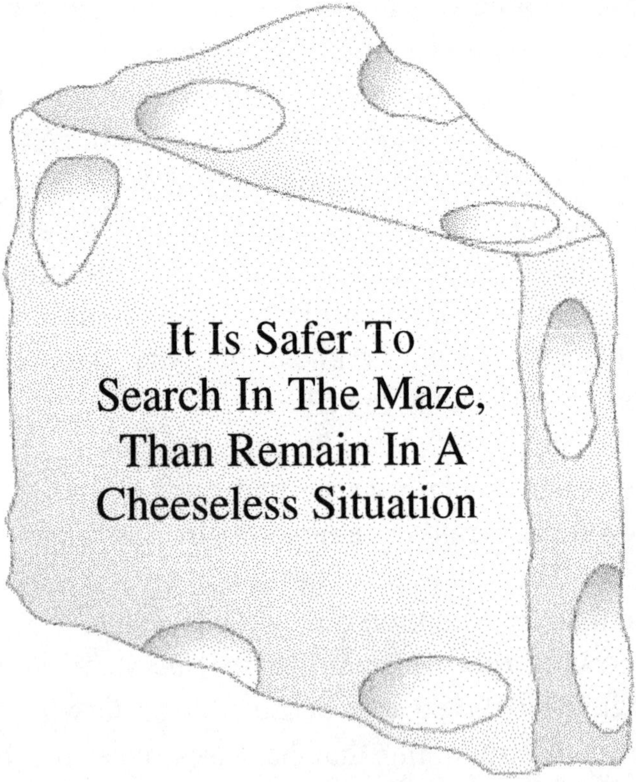

It Is Safer To
Search In The Maze,
Than Remain In A
Cheeseless Situation

He knew his old thinking was clouded by his worries and fears. He used to think about not having enough Cheese, or not having it last as long as he wanted. He used to think more about what could go wrong than what could go right.

But that had changed in the days since he had left Cheese Station C.

He used to believe that Cheese could never be moved and that change wasn't right.

Now he realized it was natural for change to continually occur, whether you expect it or not. Change could surprise you only if you didn't expect it and weren't looking for it.

He had changed his beliefs.

He paused to write on the wall:

Old Beliefs
Do Not Lead You
To New Cheese.

Haw hadn't found any Cheese yet but, as he ran through the maze, he thought about what he had already learned.

He had some new beliefs and realized he was behaving differently than when he kept returning to the same cheeseless station.

He knew when you change what you believe, you change what you do.

You can believe that change will harm you and resist it. Or you can believe that finding new cheese will help you and embrace the change.

It all depends on what you choose to believe.

He wrote on the wall:

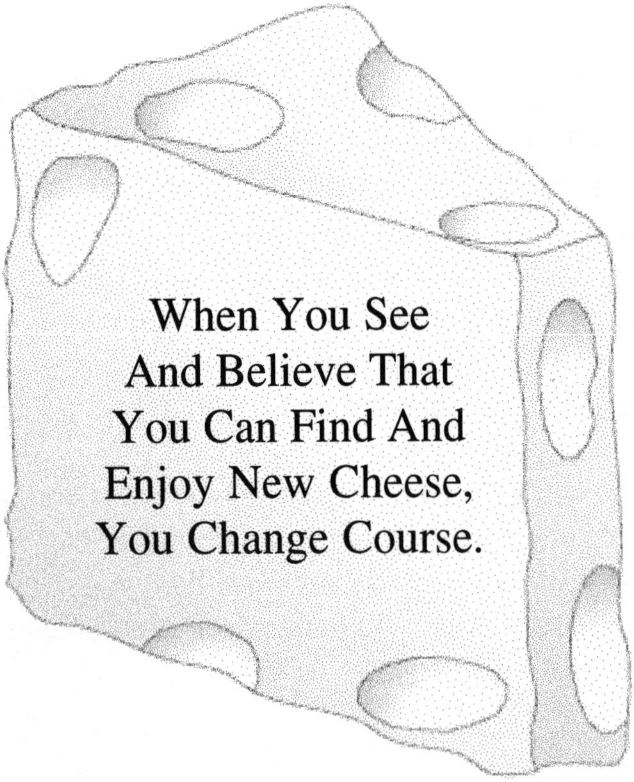

When You See
And Believe That
You Can Find And
Enjoy New Cheese,
You Change Course.

Haw knew he would be in better shape now if he had embraced the change much sooner and left Cheese Station C earlier. He would feel stronger in body and spirit and he could have coped better with the challenge of finding New Cheese. In fact, he probably would have found it by now if he had expected change, rather than wasting time denying that the change had already taken place.

He gathered his will and decided to keep proceeding into the newer parts of the maze. He found little bits of Cheese here and there and began to regain his strength and confidence.

As he thought back on where he had come from, Haw was glad he had written on the wall in many places. He trusted it would serve as a marked trail for Hem to follow through the maze, if he chose to leave Cheese Station C.

He just hoped he was heading in the right direction. He thought about the possibility that Hem would read The Handwriting On The Wall and find his way.

He wrote on the wall what he had been thinking about for some time:

Noticing
Small Changes Early
Helps You Adapt To
The Bigger Changes
That Are To Come

By now, Haw had let go of the past and was adapting to the future.

He continued on through the maze with greater strength and speed. And before long, it happened.

When it seemed like he had been in the maze forever, his journey ended quickly and happily.

Haw found New Cheese at Cheese Station N!

When he went inside, he was startled by what he saw. Piled high everywhere was the greatest supply of Cheese he had ever seen. He didn't recognize all that he saw as some kinds of Cheese were new to him.

Then he wondered for a moment whether it was real or just his imagination, until he saw his old friends Sniff and Scurry.

Sniff welcomed Haw with a nod of his head, and Scurry waved his paw. Their fat little bellies showed that they had been here for some time.

Haw quickly said his hellos and soon took bites of every one of his favorite Cheeses. He pulled off his shoes and jogging suit and folded them neatly nearby in case he needed them again. Then he jumped into the New Cheese. When he had eaten his fill, he lifted a piece of fresh Cheese and made a toast. "Hooray for Change!"

As Haw enjoyed the New Cheese, he reflected on what he had learned.

He realized that when he had been afraid to change he had been holding on to the illusion of Old Cheese that was no longer there.

So what was it that made him change? Was it the fear of starving to death? Haw thought "Well, that helped."

Then he laughed and realized that he had started to change as soon as he had learned to laugh at himself and at what he had been doing wrong. He realized the fastest way to change is to laugh at your own folly—then you can let go and quickly move on.

He knew he had learned something useful about moving on from his simple mice buddies, Sniff and Scurry. They kept life simple. They didn't overanalyze or over-complicate things. When the situation changed and the Cheese had been moved, they changed and moved with the Cheese. He would remember that.

Then Haw used his wonderful brain to do what littlepeople do better than mice.

He reflected on the mistakes he had made in the past and used them to plan for his future. He knew that you could learn to deal with change:

You could be more aware of the need to keep things simple, be flexible, and move quickly.

You did not need to over-complicate matters or confuse yourself with fearful beliefs.

You could notice when the little changes began so that you would be better prepared for the big change that might be coming.

He knew he needed to adapt faster, for if you do not adapt in time, you might as well not adapt at all.

He had to admit that the biggest inhibitor to change lies within yourself, and that nothing gets better until *you* change.

Perhaps most importantly of all, he realized that there is always New Cheese out there whether you know it at the time, or not. And that you are rewarded with it when you go past your fear and enjoy the adventure.

He knew some fear should be respected, as it can keep you out of real danger. But he realized most of his fears were irrational and had kept him from changing when he needed to change.

He didn't like it at the time, but he knew that the change had turned out to be a blessing in disguise as it led him to find better Cheese.

He had even found a better part of himself.

As Haw recalled what he had learned, he thought about his friend Hem. He wondered if Hem had read any of the sayings Haw had written on the wall at Cheese Station C and throughout the maze.

Had Hem ever decided to let go and move on? Had he ever entered the maze and discovered what could make his life better?

Haw thought about going back again to Cheese Station C to see if he could find Hem—assuming that Haw could find his way back there. If he found Hem, he thought he might be able to show him how to get out of his predicament. But Haw realized that he had already tried to get his friend to change.

Hem had to find his own way, beyond his comforts and past his fears. No one else could do it for him, or talk him into it. He somehow had to see the advantage of changing himself.

Haw knew he had left a trail for Hem and that he could find his way, if he would just read The Handwriting on the Wall.

He went over and wrote down a summary of what he had learned on the largest wall of Cheese Station N. He drew a large piece of cheese around all the insights he had learned, and smiled as he looked at what he had learned.

THE HANDWRITING ON THE WALL

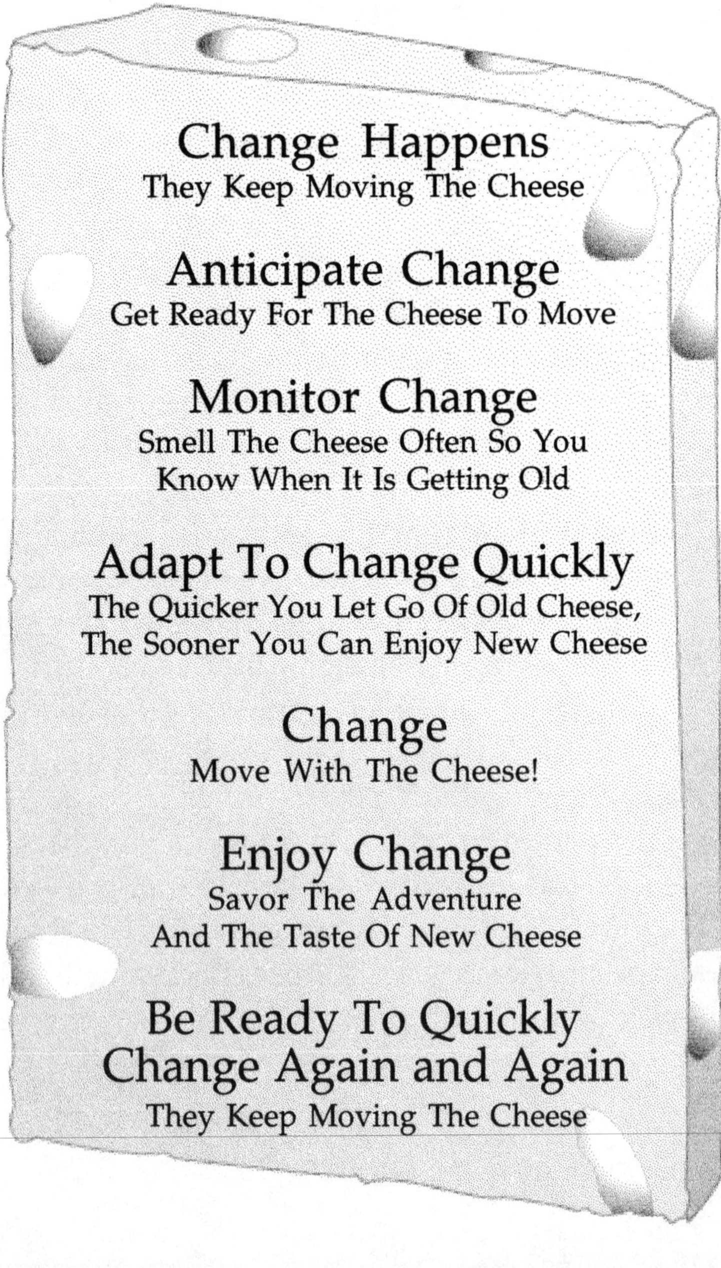

Change Happens
They Keep Moving The Cheese

Anticipate Change
Get Ready For The Cheese To Move

Monitor Change
Smell The Cheese Often So You
Know When It Is Getting Old

Adapt To Change Quickly
The Quicker You Let Go Of Old Cheese,
The Sooner You Can Enjoy New Cheese

Change
Move With The Cheese!

Enjoy Change
Savor The Adventure
And The Taste Of New Cheese

**Be Ready To Quickly
Change Again and Again**
They Keep Moving The Cheese

Haw realized how far he had come since he had been with Hem in Cheese Station C, but knew it would be easy for him to slip back if he got too comfortable. Each day he inspected Cheese Station N to see what the condition of his Cheese was. He was going to do whatever he could to avoid being surprised by unexpected change.

While Haw still had a great supply of Cheese, he often went out into the maze and explored new areas to stay in touch with what was happening around him. He knew it was safer to be aware of his real choices than to isolate himself in his comfort zone.

Haw heard what he thought was the sound of movement out in the maze. As the noise grew louder, he realized that someone was coming.

Could it be that Hem was arriving? Was he about to turn the corner?

Haw said a little prayer and hoped—as he had many times before—that maybe, at last, his friend was finally able to ...

Move With
The Cheese

And Enjoy It!

the
end

A Discussion

Later That Same Day

When Michael finished telling the story, his former classmates were smiling. Several said they got a good deal out of the story and thanked him.

Some began to say their goodbyes, as they wanted to go off and think for themselves about what they had just heard and what it meant.

Others, who wanted to discuss it, agreed to meet for a drink that evening before dinner.

Later several of them met in a hotel lounge and it wasn't long before they began to kid each other about finding their 'Cheese'.

Carlos said, "Well I'm glad I never 'Hem and Haw' when I'm faced with change." Those who knew better, shook their heads in mock disbelief.

Nathan was serious. "I wish my family had heard the Cheese story before this. Unfortunately we didn't want to see the changes coming in our business, and now it's too late—we're having to close several of our stores."

That surprised many in the group, because they thought Nathan was in a secure business, one that he could depend on year after year.

Frank, who had gone into the military added, "I hate to admit it, but I saw *myself* in the story. I usually have a good reason why change should not happen to me."

Angela said, "I didn't think it should happen to me either, but my 'Cheese' has been moved several times."

Many in the group laughed, except Nathan. He said, "Maybe, that's the whole point. It happens to all of us."

Elaine, who had been the quietest member of the class, offered, "Well, Michael, I want to thank you for telling us that story at lunch. I'm already feeling less stressed. I think as soon as I let go of some 'Old Cheese' I've been holding on to now for far too long, things are going to get a lot better."

"Good for you," Michael replied.

Elaine said, "You know, I think that's just what it's going to be—*good* for me."

Angela asked, "Do you think that Hem ever changed and moved on?"

Laura, who had joined the class part way through their senior year said, "I think he did."

"I don't think so," Cory countered. "Some people never change. And they pay a price for it. I see a lot of people like Hem in my medical practice. They feel like they are entitled to their 'Cheese'. They are angry when it's taken away and blame others. And the more upset they get, the more often they get sick."

Jessie, who had worked many different jobs and was now a salesperson, said, "I've seen the same thing. Once, at work, they gathered us together and announced that a major program we had all worked hard on was suddenly canceled. I saw several people standing around, with their hands on their hips and their jaws open, just like Hem did in the story. One of them literally yelled, 'It isn't fair!'"

Many in the group smiled, but Carlos said, "It looks funny when you see someone else doing it, but I wonder how many of us are like Hem and are just not able to laugh at ourselves?"

He added, "Hem reminded me of a friend whose department was closing down, but he didn't want to see it. They kept relocating his people. We all tried to talk to him about the many other opportunities that existed in the company for those who wanted to be flexible, but he didn't think he had to change. He was the only one who was surprised when his department closed. Now he's having a hard time adjusting."

Nathan said, "I guess it's a lot better to initiate change when you can, than it is to just try to react and adjust to it. Maybe we should be moving our own Cheese."

Frank said, "I know change is not always good. And some things never change, for example, I want to hold on to my basic values. But I realize now that I would be better off if I had moved with the 'Cheese' a lot sooner in my life."

"Well, Michael, it was a nice little story," Richard, the class skeptic, said, "but how did you actually put it into use in your company?"

The group didn't know it yet, but Richard was experiencing some changes himself. Recently separated from his wife, he was now trying to balance his career with raising his teenagers.

Michael replied, "You know, I thought my job was just to manage the daily problems as they came up when I should have been looking ahead and paying attention to where we were going.

"And boy did I manage those problems—24 hours a day. I wasn't a lot of fun to be around. I was in a rat race and I couldn't get out.

"However, after I first heard the story of 'Who Moved My Cheese?' and saw how Haw changed," Michael continued, "I realized that my job was to paint a picture of 'New Cheese.' And to do it so clearly and realistically, that I and the other people I worked with, could all enjoy changing and succeeding together."

"That's interesting," Angela said. "Because, to me, the most powerful part of the story was when Haw ran past his fear and painted a picture in his mind of finding 'New Cheese'. Running through the maze became less fearful and more enjoyable. And he eventually got a better deal."

Richard, who had been frowning during the discussion, said, "My manager's been telling me our company needs to change. I think what she's really telling me is that *I* need to, but I haven't wanted to hear it. I guess I never really knew what the 'New Cheese' was that she was trying to move us to. Or how I could gain from it."

A slight grin crossed Richard's face, as he said, "I must admit I like this idea of seeing 'New Cheese' and imagining yourself enjoying it. It lightens everything up. It lessens the fear and gets you more interested in making the change happen.

"Maybe I could use this at home. My children seem to think that nothing in their lives should ever change. They're angry. I guess they're afraid of what the future holds. Maybe I haven't painted a realistic picture of 'New Cheese' for them. Probably because I don't see it myself."

The group was quiet as several people thought about their own family life.

Then Jessie added, "Well, what I got from the story is that change is going to happen—whether I like it or not.

"I remember when our company was selling sets of encyclopedia books. One person tried to tell us that we should put our whole encyclopedia on a single computer disk and sell it for a fraction of the cost because it would cost us so much less to manufacture and so many more people could afford it. But we all resisted."

"Why did you resist?" Nathan asked.

"Because, we believed then that the backbone of our business was our large sales force who called on people door-to-door. Keeping our sales force depended on the big commissions they earned from the high price of our product. We had been doing this successfully for a long time and thought it would go on forever.

"When I think about what's happened to us, I begin to realize that it's not just that they 'moved the Cheese' but that the 'Cheese' has a life of its own and eventually runs out.

"Anyway, we didn't change. But a competitor did and now our sales are falling badly. I think I could be out of a job soon."

"It's maze time!" Carlos called out. Everyone laughed, including Jessie.

Michael complimented her, "It's good you can laugh at yourself."

Frank added, "That's what *I* got out of the story. I tend to take myself too seriously. I noticed how Haw changed when he could finally laugh at himself. No wonder he was called 'Haw'."

"Well," Elaine said, "most people here are talking about jobs, but as I listened to the story, I thought about my personal life. I think my current relationship is 'Old Cheese' that has some pretty serious mold on it."

Cory laughed in agreement. "Me too. I probably need to let go of a bad relationship."

Angela countered, "Or, perhaps the 'Old Cheese' is just old behavior. What we really need to let go of is the behavior that keeps causing our bad relationship. And then move on to a better way of thinking and acting."

"Ouch!" Cory reacted. "Good point."

Richard said, "I didn't realize it when I first heard the story, maybe because I wasn't in the mood to listen, but I'm beginning to think there may be more to it than I thought. I like the idea of letting go of old behavior instead of letting go of the relationship. Repeating the same behavior will just get you the same results."

Laura said, "I agree. As they say, 'If you do what you did, you'll get what you've got'.

"I don't know whether to laugh or cry when I hear this story," she said. "I just quit my job and now I think maybe I should have stayed and been one of the people to help my company change. I'd probably have a better job by now if I did."

Then Nathan said quietly, as though he was talking to himself, "I guess the question is, 'What do we need to let go of and what do we need to move on to?'"

No one said anything for a while. Then the conversation continued as people mentioned several other things they got out of the story.

Michael listened and liked it when people found something useful in the Cheese story the first time they heard it. He trusted that, as they reflected on it, they would get even more out of it over the years, just as he had.

Then Becky, who lived in another city but had returned for the reunion said, "As I was listening to the story and to everyone's comments here, I've had to laugh at myself. I've been like Hem for so long, hemming and hawing and afraid of change. I didn't realize how many other people did this as well. I'm afraid I've even passed it on to my children without even knowing it.

"As I think about it, I realize change really can lead you to a new and better place, although you're afraid it won't at the time.

"I remember a time when our son was a sophomore in high school. My husband's job required us to move from Illinois to Vermont and our son was upset because he had to leave his friends. He was a star swimmer and the high school in Vermont had no swim team. So, he was angry with us for making him move.

"As it turned out, he fell in love with the Vermont mountains, took up skiing, skied on his college team and now lives happily in Colorado.

"If we had all enjoyed this Cheese story together, over a cup of hot chocolate, we could have saved our family a lot of stress."

"You know," Jessie said, "this is a story you could tell to younger children, maybe an even simpler version of it. I know I wished I'd known more about these things when I was younger."

Then Frank commented, "I think I'm going to be more like Haw and move with the Cheese and enjoy it! And I'm going to pass this story along to my friends who are worried about leaving the military and what the change will mean to them. It could lead to some interesting discussions."

Michael said, "That's how we improved our business. We had several discussions about what we got from the Cheese story and how we could apply it to our own situation. It was a fun way for us all to communicate as it gave us a shorthand language. And it was very effective, especially as it spread deeper into the company."

"How so?" Nathan asked.

"Well, we discovered as we went further into our organization that the people who felt they had less power were understandably more afraid of what the change might do to them.

"When the Cheese Story was passed up and down our organization, the people who had been resisting change, became more flexible, as they saw the advantage of changing. They even helped bring about change.

"We also passed the story along to people we wanted to do business with. Then we suggested we might be their 'New Cheese.' It led to some new sales."

That gave Jessie several ideas and reminded her that she had some early sales calls in the morning. She looked at her watch and said, "Well, it's time for me to leave this Cheese Station and find some New Cheese."

The group laughed. Many of them wanted to continue the conversation, but they needed to go.

As they left they thanked Michael again. He said, "I'm very glad you found the story so useful and I hope that you will have the opportunity to share it with others."

About The Author

Spencer Johnson, M.D. is an international bestselling author whose books help millions of people discover simple truths they can use to have healthier lives with more success and less stress.

He is the Originator and co-Author of *The One Minute Manager*™, the #1 *New York Times* bestseller, written with legendary management consultant, Kenneth Blanchard, Ph.D. The book continues to appear on Business Bestseller Lists and has become the most popular management method in the world.

Dr. Johnson has written many bestsellers, including five other books in the *One Minute*® series; *Yes or No;* the popular *ValueTales*™ children's books; and the perennial gift favorite, *The Precious Present.*

His education includes a B.A. in psychology from the University of Southern California, an M.D. degree from the Royal College of Surgeons, and medical clerkships at Harvard Medical School and The Mayo Clinic.

Dr. Johnson was Medical Director of Communications for Medtronic, the inventors of cardiac pacemakers; Research Physician at The Institute for Inter-Disciplinary Studies, a think tank; and Consultant to the Center for the Study of the Person, and to the School of Medicine, University of California.

His books have been featured often in the media, including CNN, USA Today, Oprah Winfrey, The Larry King Show, Associated Press, The Washington Post, and United Press International.

There are over eleven million copies of Spencer's Johnson's books in print in twenty-six languages.

Order Form

If you would like to obtain additional copies of this book for other people to help them deal with change, you may order copies of this privately published edition
for a limited time, before the book is available in bookstores for the general public.

Please send me __________ copies
of this book at $19.95 a copy
for a total of $___________ .
(plus tax, shipping & handling)

Credit Card: Visa / Mastercard

ct. #________________________________ Expires___________

ur Signature ____

Jame: __________________________ Title: ____________________

Company: ____

treet: ____

City: ____________________________ State: _______ Zip: _______

Tel: _________________________ Fax: ______________________

To Order:

Fax This Form To:
1-808-637-7505
Or Call: 1-808-637-9030

Who Moved My Cheese?

An Amazing Way To Deal With Change
In Your Work And In Your Life

"As soon as I finished reading *Who Moved My Cheese?* I ordered copies for my entire training staff and some for my family and friends . . . a book of simple life truths . . . easy to digest . . . as applicable with changes at home as it is in handling organizational change."

Kathy Cleveland Bull
Director of Training & Development
Ohio State University

"Bravo! What wonderful insights about change. This made my move from medicine to music all the more meaningful. A fabulous read!"

Samuel Wong, M.D., Assistant Conductor
New York Philharmonic '90-'94

"I'd just learned our board had unexpectedly decided to sell the company. With no assurance of continued employment, I was depressed and playing a serious game of self pity. Then, I read *Who Moved My Cheese*. The book's message hit me like a lightening bolt! I quickly went from being angry at the unfairness of my situation to being full of confidence and keen to find my New Cheese."

Michael Carlson, President
Edison Plastics